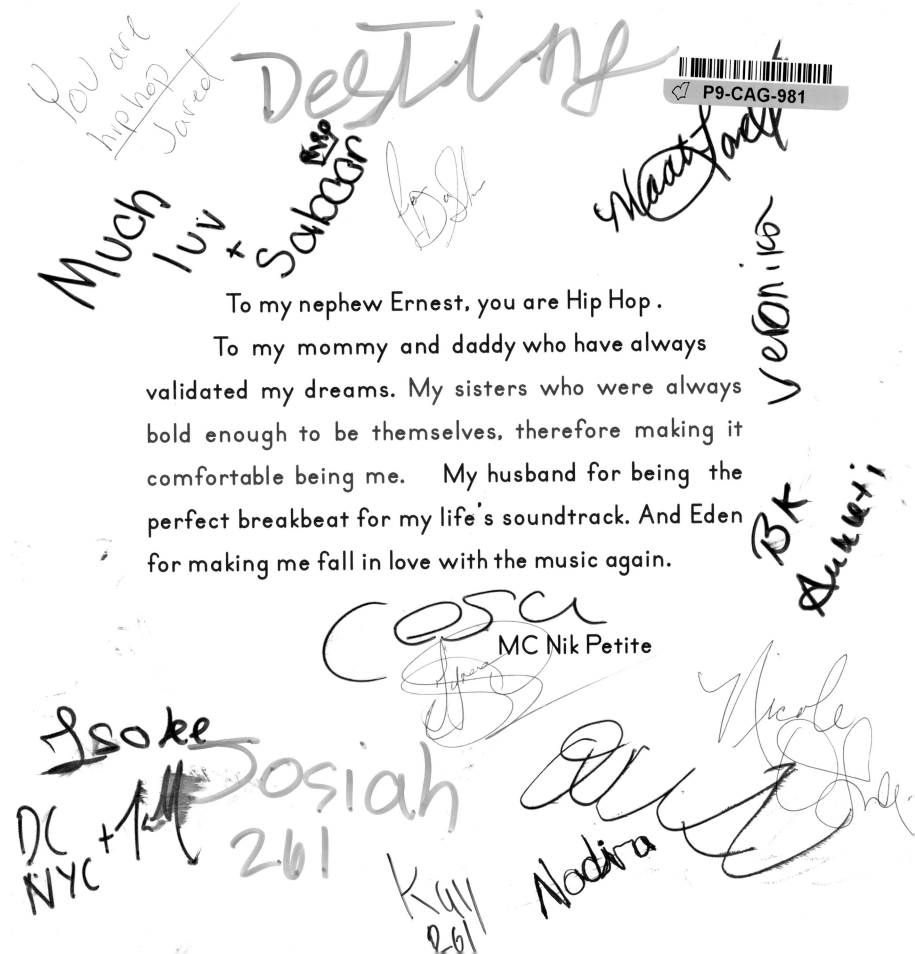

To my nephew Ernest, you are Hip Hop.
To my mommy and daddy who have always
validated my dreams. My sisters who were always
bold enough to be themselves, therefore making it
comfortable being me.   My husband for being the
perfect breakbeat for my life's soundtrack. And Eden
for making me fall in love with the music again.

MC Nik Petite

It's in the MUSIC

Whether I'm in

Or the way I Spin

the way I move my feet,

It's my creativity

and spirit.

It's more about who I am

Let's see what I am not.

I am Hip Hop!

Children in order of appearance
Cover page: Josiah "Jo Jo" Fluker McInnis
Eden Samad
Jadun Fly, Hunter Fly
(Boy climbing fence and brother)
Kartar Singh, Ajay Singh
Alyssa Sky Rebeiro (baby's feet)
Isoke Senghor
Saboor Salaam Magloire, Amoa Salaam Magloire, Khabeer
Salaam Magloire, Cesa Salaam Magloire (4 boys)
Ellis Cavendish Williams
Justice Fluker McInnis
Veronica Collin
Maeve Connolly
Tsuki Allan Smith
Naomi Boyell, Anhkh Ingall (2 chic girls)
Ellis Dulchin
Jade Williams (Brown jacket) with her sister
Julye Williams (pink jacket) girls on swings
Julien Szabados
Quinn Connolly
Dante C. Crienlow
Rhythm Salim, Journey Fujita Ajanku
(Boy with his brother on cell phone)